C902551042

D0419428

LIBRARIES NI
WITHDRAWN FROM STOCK

ANIMALS AND THEIR BABIES

HORSES AND FOALS

By Annabelle Lynch

Contents

W

FRANKLIN WATTS

LONDON·SYDNEY

GROWING INSIDE

This horse has a baby growing in her tummy. Baby horses are called **foals**.

A foal grows inside its mother for a long time. Her tummy gets bigger as the foal **grows!**

After nearly a year, the foal is ready to be **born**.

3

BEING BORN

The mother horse usually gives **birth** somewhere quiet and warm.

She often lies down to help push the foal out.

She stays close to the newborn foal to keep it warm and licks it clean.

STANDING UP

A foal can stand up an hour or two after being born. It might have to try a few times though!

Later that same day, the foal can walk and even run.

Clip! Clop!

7

DRINKING MILK

I'm hungry!

A foal is ready to eat almost as soon as it is **born**.

8

It sucks milk from its mother's teats. Most foals drink their mother's milk until they are about six months old or even older.

GRAZING

When a foal is a few weeks old, it starts eating grass. This is called grazing. It begins drinking water now, too.

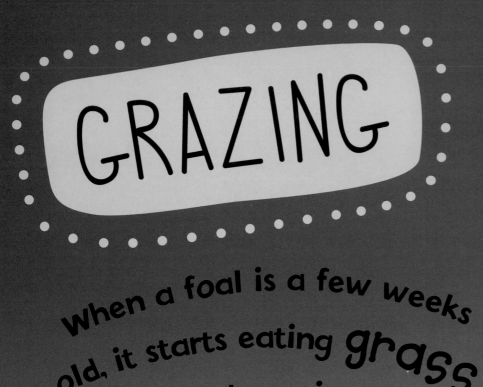

Grass is a horse's favourite food.

But they also like eating hay, oats and apples!

LEGS AND HOOVES

A newborn foal has very long legs. It is almost as **tall** as an adult horse!

Foals have **four** hooves. These are soft when a foal is born, but get harder. Hooves need to be kept healthy so the foal can walk properly as it grows up.

BROWN, BLACK OR SPOTTY

Foals are covered in
a soft, thick coat of hair.

It can be brown, black,
grey, white or spotty.
Foals are usually, but not
always, the same colour
as their mother.

Foals and horses have thick hair growing out of their neck. This is called a **mane**.

15

PLAY AND REST

As foals grow up, they should run and play outside every day. This helps them to have a **strong** and **healthy** body.

After play,
a foal needs
to get lots of
rest too!

Z

Z

Z

Z

Z

READY TO RIDE

Horses can't be ridden until they are two or three years old. You can get foals used to you by gently stroking them and talking to them.

Always make sure their **mother** is close by.

When they are ready, you can try leading them using a **halter**.

A GROWN-UP HORSE

When a foal is a year old, it is called a **yearling**. Many yearlings are ready to leave their mother and go to a new home. Others stay with their mother all their life.

When a horse is around three years old, it is ready to have **foals** of its own.

21

A HORSE'S LIFE CYCLE

newborn

A few weeks old

six months old

yearling

22

grazing

halter

hoof

WORD BANK

mane

newborn

teats

INDEX

Franklin Watts
First published in Great Britain in 2016
by The Watts Publishing Group

Copyright © The Watts Publishing Group, 2016

All rights reserved.

Series Editor: Julia Bird
Series Designer: Basement 68

Picture credits: blickwinkel/Lenz/Alamy: 23b. Agencia Fotograficzna Caro/Alamy: 4–5, 22tl, 23cr. Lars Christensen/Dreamstime: 10, 23tl. Manfred Grebler/Alamy: 22br. Svetlana Golubenko/Dreamstime: 8–9, 22tr. imagebroker/Alamy: 11. Kathryn Thorpe Klassen/Alamy: 17. Holly Kuchera/Shutterstock: 19, 23tc. mariait/Shutterstock: 16. Janian Mcmillan/Dreamstime: 6, 24. mkant/Shutterstock: 1bl, 7. Red Photography/Dreamstime: 1tr, 13, 23tr. Goce Risteski/Dreamstime: 18. Conny Sjostrom/Shutterstock: 2–3. smereka/Shutterstock: front cover. Kent Weakley/Shutterstock: 20–21, 22bl. Zoonar GmbH/Alamy: 12. Zuzule/Shutterstock: 14–15, 23cl.

Every attempt has been made to clear copyright. Should there be any inadvertent omission please apply to the publisher for rectification.

ISBN 978 1 4451 4877 9

Printed in China

FSC
www.fsc.org
MIX
Paper from responsible sources
FSC® C104740

Franklin Watts
An imprint of
Hachette Children's Group
Part of The Watts Publishing Group
Carmelite House
50 Victoria Embankment
London EC4Y 0DZ

An Hachette UK Company
www.hachette.co.uk

www.franklinwatts.co.uk